The Little
of Shape and Space

by Carole Skinner and Judith Dancer
Illustrations by Marion Lindsay

LITTLE BOOKS WITH BIG IDEAS

Featherstone Education
An imprint of Bloomsbury Publishing Plc

50 Bedford Square
London
WC1B 3DP
UK

1385 Broadway
New York
NY 10018
USA

www.bloomsbury.com
Bloomsbury is a registered trademark of Bloomsbury Publishing Plc
Text © Carole Skinner and Judith Dancer, 2015
Illustrations © Marion Lindsay, 2015
Cover photographs © LEYF/ Shutterstock

British Library Cataloguing-in-Publication Data
A catalogue record for this book is available from the British Library.

ISBN: 978-1-4729-1270-1

Library of Congress Cataloging-in-Publication Data
A catalog record for this book is available from the Library of Congress.

1 3 5 7 9 10 8 6 4 2

Printed and bound in India by Replika Pvt. Ltd

This book is produced using paper that is made from wood grown in managed, sustainable forests. It is natural, renewable and recyclable. The logging and manufacturing processes conform to the environmental regulations of the country of origin.

**To view more of our titles please visit
www.bloomsbury.com**

Contents

Introduction

Mathematics is one of the four specific areas of learning identified in the EYFS 2014 and, alongside literacy, is an area that consistently remains high on the agenda of leaders, managers and practitioners in early years settings. Shape and space is a strand of mathematics that sometimes gets overlooked in favour of counting and calculating – but it is often while engaged in activities involving shape and space that children make sense of and put to use their knowledge of similarities and differences, and the language of mathematics, both of which support their understanding of numbers.

As babies and toddlers, they will have looked at, touched, held and compared different objects – natural objects such as cones and shells; shape posting-boxes and sorters; and a huge variety of balls and beanbags to name but a few. As they do this, they begin to develop an awareness of properties such as 2D and 3D shape and pattern – a ball rolls, a box doesn't; some objects are hollow and you can fill them, others are solid. As they roll, crawl, bottom shuffle and later walk, run, jump, climb and slide, they find out more about space and position. These first moments of contact when handling and moving about are important events in children's understanding of shape and space and need to be replicated and built on in early years settings, in order for them to begin using and applying maths in real-world situations.

One of the important strategies that we can use to enrich children's learning is the sharing of expertise. Many children learn skills by observing others and by then being given the opportunity and time to rehearse those skills themselves. This book offers adult-led experiences in which practitioners can support children's understanding of shape and space, and offers a myriad of creative ideas for developing enabling environments that give children opportunities to lead and develop their own learning.

It is crucial that, in the early years, young children handle and play with lots of different types of shapes, both regular and irregular, and begin to appreciate their varying properties. Children need to build, make patterns, print with, cut apart and put back together lots of 2D and 3D shapes, so that their experiences are more than just a 'name that shape' activity. Focus on the way 3D shapes stack, roll and pack; look at how 2D shapes fit together and the spaces they leave when they don't quite fit; help children come to grips with which shapes are best to use for different purposes. With your support, children will begin to know and use the very specific vocabulary of shape, describe and discuss shapes and patterns, use simple words to describe the position of objects, and use and recognise a variety of 2D and 3D shapes in lots of different situations.

Links with the EYFS

The Characteristics of Effective Learning underpin children's development in its entirety and are essential to learning and understandings mathematics. These characteristics have been highlighted in each of the experiences and activities in this book alongside other key areas of learning, and can also be found in the following list taken from the non-statutory Development Matters guidance (DfE 2012).

▶ Finding out and exploring

▶ Playing with what they know

▶ Being willing to 'have a go'

▶ Being involved and concentrating

▶ Keeping on trying

▶ Enjoying achieving what they set out to do

▶ Having their own ideas

▶ Making links

▶ Choosing ways to do things

▶ Creating and thinking critically

▶ Thinking of ideas

▶ Finding ways to solve problems

▶ Finding new ways to do things

▶ Making links and noticing patterns in their experience

▶ Making predictions

▶ Testing their ideas

▶ Developing ideas of grouping, sequences, cause and effect

▶ Planning, making decisions about how to approach a task, solve a problem and reach a goal

▶ Checking how well their activities are going

▶ Changing strategy as needed

▶ Reviewing how well the approach worked

3D shape

A definition of a 3D shape is that it has three dimensions; that is, you can take three measurements of the shape: its height, its width and its depth. The important aspects to consider about any 3D shape are how many faces and edges the shape has, and whether or not those edges and faces are all the same shape and size. If they are, the shape will be classified as a regular shape like a cube. Alternatively, if the shape has edges that are different lengths, or faces that are different shapes, then it will be called an irregular 3D shape.

Children need plenty of experience in making models by putting together pieces from construction sets and taking them apart in order to discover and understand the properties of different 3D shapes. They will benefit from lots of play experiences that involve stacking, balancing and building with 3D shapes, including play with recycled materials. It is particularly important that you discuss 3D shape with children as they build and construct different things: encourage them to try out different shapes and decide which one is best for that specific purpose.

2D shape

The most common 2D shapes that young children work with are circles and polygons. A polygon is a 2D shape constructed of straight lines that all join up, so that the shape is closed. Polygons have different names depending on how many sides they have: a four-sided polygon, for instance, is a quadrilateral. Fortunately, young children don't need to learn all the various polygon shape names and variations in the quadrilateral group!

Children in the early years need hands-on experience of a wide range of both regular and irregular 2D shapes, in different sizes. When you are focussing on 2D shape, children will benefit enormously from making patterns, pictures and designs.

Position, direction and movement

Children need opportunities to become familiar with aspects of position, direction and movement. They should become familiar with words that are used to indicate where they are and their position in relation to others. It is not only the use of positional vocabulary such as 'next to' and 'in front of', but also directional words that describe routes, movement and journeys that children need to be confident in using. The type of experiences that children should have when they are learning about position, movement and direction are, of course, many of the things that they love to do – moving around the outdoor area on bikes, wheeling prams, chasing balls in all different directions, etc.

Pattern and symmetry

A pattern always contains elements that repeat over and over again in a predictable way. Sometimes children and even adults confuse pattern with design and will say "look at the pattern", when what they have in fact created is a design; for it to be a pattern, you need to be able to see aspects of repetition. A key element of any pattern should be that it adheres to a mathematical rule, so that when children are making patterns they are learning about applying a rule. A simple rule could be 'every other one', which could translate as a red bead, blue bead, red bead, blue bead – or a line-up that consists of an elephant, a dinosaur, an elephant, a dinosaur, and so on.

It is important that you support children in recognising and identifying the symmetrical aspects of objects they came across in day-to-day life, such as leaves, flowers, fruit and vegetables. Use a variety of media to create symmetrical designs with natural objects and make sure that children have the opportunity to look at, discuss and identify the symmetrical designs made by others.

The role of the adult

The role of the adult in supporting children's exploration and growing understanding of shape and space can be complex. As always, practitioners need to observe and tune in to children's current interests and enthusiasms, knowing when to stand back and observe, when to model vocabulary, and when to make comments or ask leading questions to challenge children's thinking. Practitioners need to:

▶ Support children in understanding and using the language of shape and space – words such as 'repeat', 'cube', 'in front of', 'behind' and 'pattern'.

▶ Challenge children by making comments such as "I'm not sure if this is the largest cube... how can we find out?"

▶ Value children's 'invented' words to describe the properties of an object in relation to shape and space – three 'joiners' (corners), or a 'fat square' (cube).

▶ Plan experiences to offer children opportunities to develop their ideas about shape and space.

▶ Share picture books and read story books with elements of shape and space, including position, direction and pattern, with a focus on the pattern in stories such as 'We're going on a Bear Hunt'.

▶ Point out shapes and patterns in the environment – windows, doors, tiles, bricks, and road signs.

▶ Involve children in putting together interactive displays of activities and experiences linked to work on exploring shape and space.

- ▶ Act as a co-player with children as they are playing with shapes and fitting shapes together, doing simple jigsaws and using shape posting boxes, and using construction sets and making models from junk materials.

- ▶ Identify opportunities to explore shape and space in everyday activities e.g. snack time, or tidying up, packing things away and fitting things in boxes.

- ▶ Ensure children have lots of opportunities to explore shape and space on a large scale and using their whole bodies – e.g. inventing and describing movements by turning their body in different ways.

- ▶ Identify symmetry in natural objects and drawing children's attention to it.

Vocabulary of 3D shape
Solid shape, hollow shape, cube, cuboid, pyramid, cylinder, sphere, edge, corner, face, same, different.

Vocabulary of 2D shape
Flat shape, circle, triangle, square, rectangle, hexagon, side, corner.

Vocabulary of position, movement and direction
Straight line, curved line, forwards, backwards, route, pathway, start, stop, position, arrow, follow, finish, end, under, over, next, in front of, behind, start from, to, along, above, inside, outside, up, down, next to, between.

Vocabulary of pattern and symmetry
Match, shape, same, different, first, second, last, next, pattern, repeat, fold, rough, smooth, soft, hard, shiny, dull, copy.

How this book is organised

This book is split into four sections that reflect the shape and space aspects identified in the Early Years Foundation Stage:

- ▶ Section one: 3D shape

- ▶ Section two: 2D shape

- ▶ Section three: Position, direction and movement

- ▶ Section four: Pattern and symmetry

Each activity follows the same format, but is not prescriptive because we all know that flexibility is key in the early years and that young children, by their very nature, are unpredictable.

Each activity identifies elements of both Enabling Environments and Positive Relationships, including specific vocabulary that can be introduced and modelled, alongside open-ended questions and enabling comments. Each experience includes:

► What's the learning?

► What you could provide;

► What you could do;

► What you could say;

► Another great idea.

Essential resources

Children need to have access to the following resources to successfully develop concepts about shape and space:

► Recycled materials to build with

► Commercially-produced construction equipment, both large and small, including small bricks, blocks and cubes

► Items to thread – plastic cotton reels, beads, natural objects, buttons

► Climbing equipment to explore

► Materials that changes shape – clay, play dough and plasticine

► Mark-making materials – chalk, paint, water and brushes, pencils, charcoal, sand, cornflour, mud, hypoallergenic shaving foam, finger paint

► Fruit and vegetables to explore e.g. at snack time and in cooking experiences

► Small world play resources

► Roadways, train tracks and materials to create pathways and routes

► A range of materials to create patterns with – shells, pebbles, conkers, fir cones, buttons, bangles

► Reference books and story books which explore aspects of shape and space

► Mirrors, mirror tiles, light box

► 2D shapes – plastic, card, wood

► Hollow and solid 3D shapes – plastic and wood

► Things to fill and empty – boxes, cylinders, some with removal lids

► Fabrics with repeating patterns

Useful vocabulary for practitioners

3D shapes are classified according to how many faces the shape has:

Number of faces	Shape name
1	sphere
4	tetrahedron
5	pentahedron
6	hexahedron
7	septahedron
8	octahedron
9	nonahedron
10	decahedron
11	undecahedron
12	dodecahedron
20	icosahedron

Polygons (2D shapes that have straight sides and are closed) are classified according to how many sides the shape has:

Number of sides	Shape name
3	triangle
4	quadrilateral (in this group are squares, rectangles and rhombuses)
5	pentagon
6	hexagon
8	octagon
10	decagon

SECTION ONE:
3D SHAPE

Moving house

All children love hiding and playing inside boxes – and when they have finished, jumping on boxes and flattening them is great fun. In this experience, children can reconstruct the boxes before jumping into or on top of them!

What's the learning?

3D shape names and properties; playing with what they know and testing their ideas

What you could provide:

▶ Several assorted huge cuboid boxes, flattened so that they can be re-constructed

▶ Masking tape, marking pens and scissors

What you could do:

▶ Lay the flattened boxes on the ground.

▶ Observe the children as they explore the flattened cuboid boxes – are the boxes all the same?

- Encourage the children to work together collaboratively to construct the boxes, using masking tape to hold the sides in place.
- If children get stuck, suggest a range of strategies, including reviewing what they have already done and achieved.
- Note the ways in which children make decisions about how to approach the task, negotiate and reach their goal.

What you could say:

- Talk to the children about their earlier home experiences – how many children remember moving house and using packing boxes?
- Introduce and model the use of the language of 3D shape: hollow, cube, cuboid, edge, corner, face, same, different.
- Discuss which shape the flat cardboard could be made into.
- Support the children's own conversations about what they are doing and why.
- Help the children to express their mathematical thinking as they re-construct the boxes: "What do you think you need to do next?"; "How could you fix that edge?"
- Support the children as they describe and discuss the boxes and collaborate to fix them together.
- Talk to the children about other cubes and cuboids in the setting, e.g. construction blocks.

Another great idea:

- Introduce 'moving day' role-play into the home corner and add a 'Sold' sign.
- Set up a 'new home' outdoors – either a playhouse or a temporary outdoor home corner.
- Provide the constructed boxes from the main activity, along with bubble wrap, wrapping paper, washable markers and sticky tape.
- Support children as they wrap home corner items, fill boxes and label the contents, then encourage them to work together to move the boxes from the 'old house' to the 'new house'.
- Talk about the contents of boxes – make links between weight and size.

Goldilocks Ltd.

This experience builds on children's understanding of the traditional and ever-popular story of 'Goldilocks and the Three Bears'.

What's the learning?

3D shape names and properties; choosing ways to do things

What you could provide:

▶ Several large identical cardboard boxes (one per group)

▶ Masking tape, scissors, glue

▶ Wallpaper and paste

▶ A floor covering

What you could do:

▶ Introduce the activity to small groups of children: they should work together to construct a house for the three bears. Each group should decide how many doors and windows they think are needed. Can they make separate rooms in the house? How many rooms are needed?

- Provide each group with a cardboard box and make sure the masking tape, scissors and glue are readily available. Support the children in their construction.

- When complete, re-group as a class to discuss what materials the children will need for decorating the houses.

- Observe which children use a 'trial and error' approach and which children try to predict the amount of paper needed to decorate each room. Note how children choose the amount of paper they will use and how they explain their selection.

- As children are cutting the paper, encourage them to discuss the best way to predict how much is needed.

- Note children who persist with the activity when challenges occur and those who use alternative approaches.

What you could say:

- Clarify the challenge with the children – this is about designing and decorating a house for the three bears.

- Talk about the size of house needed – they might want to create a kitchen, lounge, bathroom and bedrooms.

- Discuss the type of wallpaper that Baby Bear might want for his bedroom – what about Daddy Bear? And what might go in the kitchen?

- Ask questions such as "How much paper do you need to wallpaper the lounge?"; "Is that enough paper?"; "Do you need the same amount of paper for the bedroom, or more, or less?"

- Make connections with the children's home experiences – have they ever chosen wallpaper or carpet for their own bedroom at home?

- Make comments about what you are doing – "I wonder if there is enough blue carpet for the lounge floor?"

- Provide scaffolding for children's own questions and support them as they answer each others' questions.

Another great idea:

- Build up collections of small boxes, cylinders and other recycled materials, then provide three different sized bears and set challenges for the children, for example : build one table for all three bears; build a chair for Mummy Bear/ Daddy Bear/ Baby Bear; build a bed for Mummy Bear/ Daddy Bear/ Baby Bear.

Cooking shapes

Cooking is always a favourite activity, especially if the results can be taken proudly home to share with the family. These bread rolls are quick and easy to make and the children will be able to take them home at the end of the session.

What's the learning?

Using the vocabulary of 3D shape; enjoying achieving what they set out to do

What you could provide:

▶ Enough ingredients for about 20 rolls:
  ▷ 500g strong white bread flour
  ▷ 300ml warm water
  ▷ 1 sachet fast-action dried yeast
  ▷ 1 tablespoon olive oil
  ▷ 1 teaspoon of salt
▶ Mixing bowl, pastry boards
▶ Knives, play dough tools

- ► Cling film
- ► Timer
- ► Extra flour for the boards
- ► Baking tray

What you could do:

- ► Introduce the bread roll making activity to a small group.
- ► Measure out all of the ingredients into a large bowl, and allow the children to combine them together using one kneading movement each (you may need to finish the kneading yourself to make a total of about 30 movements).
- ► Leave the dough for 10 minutes (allow the children to set the timer) and then knead again using 30 movements. In this time, encourage the children to decide what shape roll to make. Aim for a selection of different shapes.
- ► After the second round of kneading, count together how many children are in the group, and divide the dough accordingly so each child has one piece.
- ► Encourage the children to form their dough into different shaped rolls.
- ► When the rolls are made, cover with a piece of oiled cling film and leave to prove in a warm place (on top of the pre-heating oven works well) for 30 minutes until roughly doubled in size.
- ► Show the children how much the rolls have grown in size and shape. Place on a greased baking tray and bake at 220°C/ Gas Mark 7 for 15 minutes.

What you could say:

- ► Introduce and model the use of descriptive vocabulary: "I am going to make my roll quite round and smooth."
- ► Support the children's own descriptions about the shapes they are making with their dough.
- ► Initiate discussions about the similarities and differences between the shapes of the rolls they are making.
- ► Make comments such as: "I wonder what shape you are going to make with your dough?"
- ► Increase and share the group knowledge by summarising some of the actions that the children make when working with their dough. "I noticed that some of you are rolling your dough into long cylinders and then twisting them into circles."

Another great idea:

▶ Assemble a range of shop-bought rolls and compare and contrast their different shape and sizes. Discuss and decide where to cut each roll in half and talk about the shape of each half-roll. Spread the half-rolls with cream cheese or other topping of choice and eat!

▶ Use tortilla wraps as thin pizza bases and let each pair of children co-operate and share the making of their pizza. Spread each tortilla with tomato sauce and sprinkle with grated cheese. Ask the children to add toppings such as tinned sweetcorn, slices of mushroom, and use cutters to create vegetable shapes. Draw their attention to the irregular shapes of some of the toppings and together invent names for the shapes. Cook the pizzas for 8 – 10 minutes at 220°C/Gas Mark 7.

'Can you find the 3D shape?'

This game helps children to identify the 2D face on a 3D shape by giving them lots of opportunities to handle real objects.

What's the learning?

Identifying 2D shapes on 3D objects and making links between the two

What you could provide:

▶ A large shape spinner with a square, circle, triangle and rectangle on it. (You could use a large dice instead and stick one of each shape on each side of the dice).

▶ A collection of real objects where, for each object, the shape of at least one face is shown on your shape spinner.

▶ A set of 3D shapes or bricks including cubes, pyramids, cylinders, cuboids and any other 3D shape where at least one face is shown on your shape spinner.

▶ A box to contain all the objects and shapes.

What you could do:

▶ Look at the objects in the box together, and ask the children to take them out one at a time.

▶ Encourage the children to say something about the object they are holding; they could offer the name of the object, whether they have one at home, what it is used for, or they could simply name the colour or texture.

▶ Draw the children's attention to the name and shape of their object. Encourage them to run their finger round the edge of one of the object's faces.

▶ When the children have explored the objects, put them back in the box and play the following game.

▶ The children should choose a mixture of 3D shapes and real objects from the box so they each have four in total. They take it in turns to spin the spinner. If the spinner shows the face of one of their shapes or objects they put it back in the box. Keep spinning until the children have put all the shapes back in the box.

What you could say:

▶ Support those children who need it by identifying the shape on the spinner: "Look, a square... can you see a square on your object?"

▶ Give visual aid by drawing the shape in the air as you say the name.

▶ Emphasise properties of particular shapes as you discuss them: "Mmm, a triangle – that's the shape with three corners, isn't it?"

Another great idea:

▶ Play "Musical 'Pass the Shape'". The children sit in a small circle and pass a shape or an object around. When the music stops, the child holding it says a property of the shape, or the name, or something about the object.

▶ Play "Hunt the Shape": hide some shapes such as triangles in the outdoor area and ask the children to search and find as many as they can. You could provide a card with a picture of the shape they are searching for on it, or give them a similar shape to hold and compare with what they are looking for.

Cylinder build

Cylinders are not often incorporated into children's construction play, other than as a finishing touch on top of a castle or bridge. Use this activity to help children explore the properties and potential of cylinders.

What's the learning?

Properties of 3D shape; finding out and exploring

What you could provide:

▶ A collection of solid cylinders such as empty cans, wooden bricks and rolling pins

▶ Hollow cardboard cylinders of different sizes

▶ Paper clips, PVA glue, sticky tape

▶ Post-it notes

▶ Pieces of thin rectangular card

▶ Play dough and rolling pins

▶ Scissors

What you could do:

▶ Establish the differences and the similarities between the cylinders. Together, sort them into solid and hollow cylinders.

- ▶ Discuss the properties of the cylinders with the children; emphasise that although they are all different sizes and heights, they are all called cylinders.
- ▶ Identify cylinders as having three faces. Use hands and fingers to show that there are two flat circles and one curved face.
- ▶ Encourage the children to cut one of the hollow cylinders along its edge and show how it unwraps to become a rectangle.
- ▶ Invite the children to look and see if they can find any corners on a cylinder.
- ▶ Show the children how to wrap a sticky note around their finger and stick it down to make a hollow cylinder.
- ▶ Help children to slice cylinders to make smaller cylinders, and make sure that it is an active learning construction experience for all the children.
- ▶ Provide play dough for the children to make solid cylinders with.
- ▶ Suggest you all make one large construction using cylinders. Remind them that they can use rectangles of paper or card to make more cylinders.

What you could say:

- ▶ "I wonder what shape this cylinder will be if I cut it open?"
- ▶ "I think this is a hollow cylinder... how can we find out?"
- ▶ "Can you explain the difference between a hollow cylinder and a solid cylinder?"
- ▶ Encourage listening and questioning between the children to promote their confidence and self-esteem, as well as developing their mathematical understanding.
- ▶ Encourage the children to continue to explore and experiment with the properties of a cylinder as they make their construction.

Another great idea:

- ▶ Assemble an interactive display of cylinders of different sizes and materials, both hollow and solid, and invite the children to construct and play with them. Include wheels, buttons and empty tins as well as the more conventional cardboard tubes and wooden bricks. Demonstrate how the wheels and buttons are still cylinders, despite having a very thin curved faced between the two flat circles at either end.
- ▶ Outdoors, assemble lots of different tunnels, tubes, pipes and other cylinders for children to crawl along and through or post things down.

Making a toy box

Inviting children to bring a much-loved toy from home helps build links between family and school, especially for those children who in the early days in a setting need reassurance. You should, of course, make sure that there is also a supply of soft toys for those who forget, or leave their toy at home.

What's the learning?

3D shape; choosing ways to do things

What you could provide:

▶ A collection of recycled boxes of different shapes and sizes

▶ Some soft toys

▶ A range of coloured paper, pieces of material and scraps of felt

▶ Glue and sticky tape

▶ Plastic 2D shapes

▶ Measuring tapes

▶ Pencils, pens, scissors, stapler

▶ Ribbons and/or small pieces of string

What you could do:

▶ Suggest that the children make a carrying box for their toy. Observe how they use the materials and their level of skill when using equipment such as staplers and scissors.

▶ Support them in choosing a box that their toy will fit into. Demonstrate and encourage the children to explore how the different boxes open and close.

▶ Encourage them to explain why they chose that particular box.

▶ Talk about covering the box and offer different fabrics to cover the box in.

▶ Model how to draw around the faces of each box onto the material, cut out the shapes and stick them on the faces of the box.

▶ Challenge the children to add handles, using ribbon or string, so that they can carry their decorated box around the setting and/or home.

What you could say:

▶ Introduce and use the language of shape, using comparative mathematical language to describe the size of the boxes: "This box looks much longer than that one..."

▶ Extend children's learning by asking questions such as: "What can you say about the shape of your box?"

▶ Make comments as you are drawing around the box: "If I draw around this face I think it should be the right size... what do you think?"

▶ Provide scaffolding for children's own questions and actions: "How did you decide what size to cut the fabric?"

Another great idea:

▶ Use recycled boxes to make a village for small world characters. Provide paints and brushes for children to decorate the boxes. First cut the boxes along two connected edges and turn the boxes inside-out and re-assemble. In this way, the children can paint the plain inside of the box.

▶ Make an interactive display with a collection of small boxes and natural and man-made materials such as acorns, shells and pennies, and invite children to fill and empty the boxes. Encourage them to decide which one of the boxes is the most suitable container for each of the different sets of objects.

Lids off!

This activity takes advantage of children's delight in finding lost items, and will soon become a firm favourite.

What's the learning?

Shape; choosing ways to do things

What you could provide:

▶ A collection of everyday containers with removable lids, in different shapes and sizes

▶ An empty box to put the lids in

What you could do:

▶ Before the session starts, remove all the lids and put all but one of them in a separate box. Hide one of the lids.

▶ Ask for help in sorting the lids and suggest that one might be missing. Show the children the box of lids and ask them to match each lid with a container.

- Observe which children use the language of shape in conversation.
- Notice if any of the children have a strategy for deciding whether there is a missing lid, e.g. counting containers and lids, or quickly pairing lids with containers.
- Play a game of 'find which lid is missing' with the children. Once they have identified the container that has a missing lid, continue the game by taking it in turns to hide one or two lids while the rest of the group identify which container or containers are missing them.

What you could say:

- Ask questions such as: "I wonder why this lid doesn't fit the jar?"
- "How can we find out if a container is missing a lid?"
- Provide and extend the vocabulary of shape and model the language of movement by making comments such as: "I think this lid needs twisting all the way round so that it will stay on..."
- Invite the children to suggest what the contents or the purpose of the containers could be: "I wonder if this would be a good jar to keep bread in?"
- Draw children's attention to the similarities and differences between the containers. "What sort of lid do you think this long box needs?"

Another great idea:

- Introduce a variety of small sorting items that the children can use to fill the containers, including uncooked rice and green lentils, which can be poured easily into the containers using funnels.
- Resource an area with a range of different sized tongs for the children to pick up larger items.
- Provide large sticky notes for the children to attach to the containers, detailing the contents. Make links between the shape, size and weight of the different containers.
- Suggest that the children line up a row of full and nearly full containers, then provide beaters and encourage the children to make music!

SECTION TWO:
2D SHAPE

Kim's game

All children love hiding things. In this game, the children will practise making predictions and developing strategies to help them remember.

What's the learning?

2D shape names; being involved; concentrating

What you could provide:

► A tray
► 2D triangles, squares, rectangles and circles in different colours, sizes and/or textures
► A cloth or teatowel

What you could do:

► Spread out the 2D shapes on the tray.
► Give the children opportunities to explore the shapes and describe them: "This is a very small circle"; "This is a shiny square"; "This is a very rough triangle".

- ▶ Put the shapes back onto the tray, ask the children to cover their eyes, and remove one of the shapes.

- ▶ Cover the tray for a short time.

- ▶ When you uncover the tray, give the children a little while to consider which shape is missing, then encourage them to talk in pairs before asking them for their responses.

- ▶ Observe the strategies used by the children – who is methodical? Who calls out the name of a shape randomly?

- ▶ Model again several times, and then let a child take the lead.

What you could say:

- ▶ Introduce and model the use of the language of 2D shape: 'triangle', 'square', 'rectangle', 'circle', 'edge', 'corner', 'same', 'different'.

- ▶ Discuss what words could describe each shape: 'rough', 'shiny', 'small', 'long'.

- ▶ Support children's own conversations about which shape is missing.

- ▶ Help the children to express their mathematical strategies, when they identify the correct shape: "Yes, that's right, it is the red circle, how did you remember that?" Offer prompts where necessary: "So did you know how many circles there were altogether?"

Another great idea:

- ▶ Make some A4 laminated cards with different shapes on and some 'hiding cards' – cards that each have a different sized 'peep hole' cut out in the middle.

- ▶ Place one 'peep hole' card over a shape card – exposing just one part of the shape.

- ▶ Ask the children to predict which shape they think is hidden and why, i.e. using prompts such as: "It's got a straight edge, so could it be a circle?"

- ▶ Show another part of the shape and ask the children to reconsider, e.g. "It's got a corner a bit like a square – oh, but could it be a triangle?"

Flour paste prints

Most children like suprises, and many enjoy taking part in creative activities. This experience offers opportunities to work together and have some fun while finding out more about the 2D shapes on the faces of 3D shapes.

What's the learning?

2D and 3D shape names; planning how to reach a goal; collaboration

What you could provide:

▶ Assorted small solid cubes, pyramids and cylinders

▶ Plain flour and water

▶ Mixing bowl and spoon

▶ Shallow trays

▶ A large piece of white cotton fabric

▶ Cold water dye

What you could do:

▶ Introduce the activity to a small group of children: you will be looking at the faces of the 3D shapes.

- ▶ Mix the water and the flour together until it forms a thick paste – give the children opportunities to predict how much water is needed and to stir the mixture. Pour the thick mixture into the shallow trays.
- ▶ Support the children as they use the flour paste to coat one face of their chosen solid shape and use it to print onto the cotton fabric.
- ▶ Continue until most of the fabric is covered with flour paste prints.
- ▶ Hang the fabric outside until all of the flour paste is dry.
- ▶ Soak the fabric in coloured cold-water dye, following directions and ensuring children's clothing is protected.
- ▶ When the dying is complete, wash the fabric in a machine to remove all of the flour paste. Ask the children to predict what will happen (white prints remain when the paste washes away).
- ▶ When the fabric is dry, explore it with the children and give them opportunities to match the 3D shapes to the 2D prints.

What you could say:

- ▶ Model the use of 2D and 3D shape – focusing on 'faces'.
- ▶ Ask questions such as "So why do you think that pyramid could match a square shape?"
- ▶ During the printing make comments about what you are doing – "I wonder if there is enough space there for another triangle shape?"; "If the big square won't fit, do you think the small circle will?"
- ▶ Provide scaffolding for the children's own questions and support them as they answer each others' questions.

Another great idea:

- ▶ Introduce 'tie dye' to the children.
- ▶ Make or provide a collection of solid cubes.
- ▶ Support children as they use tape, elastic bands or thick string to fix one, two or three cubes into individual pieces of cotton fabric, about 30cm square.
- ▶ When you have lots of squares of fabric with cubes securely fixed in each, put half of the fabric squares into one colour dye and half into another.
- ▶ When the squares are dry, remove the string, elastic bands, tape and blocks to see the shapes that have been created.
- ▶ Once dry, create a patchwork pattern with the children by sewing the fabric squares together to make a table cover for your setting.

Spiders' webs

Children are endlessly intruiged by the natural world, and spiders' webs are particularly fascinating. Children's interest and observations can be a great way in to discussing symmetry and connectors.

What's the learning?

Position, direction and movement; making links and noticing patterns in their experiences

What you could provide:

▶ Paper circles or circles cut from plastic folders

▶ Watered-down PVA glue in squirty bottles

▶ Plastic spiders

▶ Glitter

▶ Blu-Tack

What you could do:

▶ Start a discussion by looking for a spider's web in your outdoor area, or else find pictures in nature books or a video clip on YouTube.

- ▶ Suggest that the children make their own spiders' webs and demonstrate by squirting glue in spiral movements on one of the circles, then in straight lines to make connectors on the web.
- ▶ Challenge the children to create their own spiders' webs: they can sprinkle glitter to give the effect of dew if they wish.
- ▶ When the glue has dried, carefully peel off the paper and suspend on a washing line or Blu-Tack to a window, complete with plastic spiders.

What you could say:

- ▶ Make comments about and compare the number of turns in the children's webs, and refer to how many connectors they drew across their webs.
- ▶ Ask questions such as: "How big do you think the biggest spider's web we can make will be?" "How many spirals do you think it will have?"
- ▶ Introduce mathematical language such as 'spiral', 'straight' and 'curved lines'.

Another great idea:

- ▶ Collect three small sticks. Tie them together with an elastic band into a star shape. Provide the children with wool or thick string that they can weave in and out of the sticks to make a different type of spider's web. Use PVA glue to attach the ends of the wool to the sticks, to stop the webs unravelling.
- ▶ Chalk a large spider's web on the ground in the outdoor area, and encourage a long line of children to walk round the spiral to the centre of the web.
- ▶ Give each child a piece of paper and scissors and show them how to cut out a spiral snake. Provide pens so that they can draw eyes and a mouth on their snakes.
- ▶ Make apple peel spirals, print spirals on paper, thread pasta spirals and encourage children to create their own spirals using a range of media.
- ▶ Read 'The Very Busy Spider' by Eric Carle together, as well as some of the many Anansi stories.
- ▶ Sing and dramatise the nursery rhyme 'Incy Wincy Spider'.

Tessellating shapes

Help the children discover which shapes fit together to make another shape, and which tessellate if you join them together to form a repeating pattern with no gaps or overlaps.

What's the learning?

Exploring and fitting 2D shapes together; keeping on trying

What you could provide:

▶ A selection of different shapes in a range of materials, colours, sizes and textures

What you could do:

▶ Look at and handle all of the shapes together. Draw attention to their different properties.

▶ Allow the children to choose a selection of shapes. Encourage them to explore and describe the similarities and differences of the shapes they are working with.

▶ Suggest that the children each choose a selection of one shape and see if these same shapes fit together without any gaps (tessellate).

▶ Work with the children to discover if any new shapes can be made by fitting two shapes together.

What you could say:

▶ Support the children in verbalising their mathematical thinking.

▶ "Could you explain how you decided to use those shapes to make your pattern?"

▶ "Has anyone else found out that squares will fit together without leaving any gaps?"

▶ "I wonder what shape you can make if you put two triangles together?"

▶ Help the children as they describe their patterns by offering new vocabulary or inviting a child to describe another's pattern or design.

▶ At the end of the session, summarise what you've learnt: "I've learnt that if I put the hexagons together then there won't be any gaps. Did anyone else learn that?"

Another great idea:

▶ Gather together a collection of different objects and shapes and place in a pillowcase or bag.

▶ Challenge the children to take turns at putting their hands inside the pillowcase to feel one of the objects, and ask them to describe and make guesses about what the shape is before bringing it out of the pillowcase.

▶ Support the children in elaborating on their descriptions by modelling mathematical words, for instance: "Has your object got any curves, or is it made up of straight lines and corners like a square?"

▶ Use a large book as a screen and position the shape from the pillowcase behind it so that a small part peeps out from behind the screen. Ask children to describe what they see and to suggest what shape might be behind the screen. Also invite them to say what shape or object it can't possibly be.

▶ You could extend the activity by playing a shape-based game of 'I Spy'. Search for a triangle, cube, cylinder or any other shape that the children are familiar with.

Fruit boxes

This game is a fun and effective way of getting children to learn the vocabulary of shape. It is especially helpful for speakers of English as an Additional Language (EAL) due to the repetition during play and the visual clues that accompany the vocab.

What's the learning?

Recognising and using 2D shape words; making links

What you could provide:

▶ Three large shapes (triangle, square and circle), cut from paper
▶ A numeral dice 1-3
▶ A shape dice with triangle, square and circle, each shown twice
▶ Twenty-one pieces of plastic fruit from a sorting set, placed in a basket (you could replace with twenty-one of any other item if more convenient)

What you could do:

▶ Play this game with a group of four children.
▶ Put the three paper shapes and the basket of plastic fruit shapes in the middle of the table.

- Encourage the children to take it in turns to roll both dice (numeral and shape) and to read out the number and the shape shown on the dice.

- Each child should pick up pieces of fruit according to the number shown on the numeral dice, and put them on the paper shape that matches the shape shown on the shape dice.

- They keep taking turns until all the fruit from the basket has gone.

- At the end of the game, encourage the children to count how many pieces of fruit are on each shape, to see which has the most and which has the fewest.

What you could say:

- Support the children in reading and interpreting the dice. Emphasise the rule that you must say out loud the number and the shape that you roll. In this way children hear the vocabulary repeated.

- Ask: "What does each dice show?"; "So what are you going to do?"

- Check that the children understand the rules: "Can you explain how to play the game?"

- Think aloud: "I wonder which shape has the most fruit on? Has anyone got any idea how we can find out?"

Another great idea:

- Play again and, this time begin the game with the fruit evenly distributed across each of the paper shapes; ask the children to do this and observe what strategies and ideas they use. When each of the shapes has seven pieces of fruit on it, play 'emptying the shapes' by throwing both the dice and taking the specified number of plastic fruit shapes off the correct paper shape and putting them back in the basket.

- Play the game again but this time use a 1-6 dice and more pieces of plastic fruit.

- Suggest that the children decide which shapes to use next time you play the game. You might offer 'hexagon', 'rectangle' and 'oval' if they are unsure which to choose.

- For children who need further support, the focus could be colour instead of shape. Alternatively, try using 3D shape names with the aim of putting the objects in the appropriate-shaped boxes.

Jaws

Young children love to run around outdoors, make noise and be a little bit scared in a 'safe' situation. This game gives them the chance to do all three!

What's the learning?

2D shape; changing strategy as needed

What you could provide:

▶ Playground chalks
▶ Soundtrack from 'Jaws' and method of playing

What you could do:

▶ Using chalk, draw some large shapes in different colours (big enough for about four children to stand in) on a tarmac or paved area outdoors. These are your 'life rafts'. Make sure you include the same shapes in more than one colour.

▶ Talk to the children about the game. The idea is that children move around the outdoor area when the music plays, and when it stops they have to move to the correct life raft according to the shape you have called out, to escape the 'shark'.

▶ Encourage the children to explore different ways of travelling as the music plays, e.g. star jumps, sidesteps, hopping, skipping.

▶ Stop the music and call out one shape name.

▶ Any child who doesn't choose the correct shape is 'eaten' and sits out in the next session.

▶ Repeat, limiting the number of life rafts by naming a colour as well as a shape – for example, calling out 'red square' or 'green circle'.

▶ When only a few children are left, limit the number of children allowed on each life raft to one or two.

What you could say:

▶ Talk to children about the rules of the game.

▶ Model the use of the language of shapes: 'circle', 'triangle', 'square'.

▶ Encourage children to discuss how many children can fit onto each shape.

Another great idea:

▶ Make a stepping stones game with the children, using coloured playground chalk.

▶ Choose a 'start zone' and a 'finish zone'.

▶ Now draw equal numbers of squares, circles and triangles between the start and finish zones, making sure that children can jump from one shape to another to travel all the way from start to finish.

▶ Encourage the children to take turns in groups of three to travel from the start to the finish zone – one child only jumps on circles, another only on squares and another only on triangles.

▶ Talk to the children about the stepping stone routes being 'fair': "Are there an equal number of circles, squares and triangles?"

Round and round

This experience gives children lots of time to explore mark-making outdoors by trying out ways of drawing circles on the ground and on vertical paper.

What's the learning?

2D shape; making decisions about how to approach a task

What you could provide:

▶ Shallow trays with squirts of two colours of ready-mixed paint
▶ Wide brushes
▶ Strips of lining paper
▶ Playground chalks
▶ Water
▶ Buckets
▶ Decorators' brushes

What you could do:

▶ Make sure all of the children have enough space and ask them to make a huge circle in the air with their finger – model doing this, and as they keep drawing the circle in the air say "round and round". Then ask children to make the circle the other way (i.e. clockwise, reversed to anti-clockwise). Repeat with the other arm.

▶ Now divide the children into groups of three and share the following three activities between them: one group painting circles with paint, another drawing circles on the floor with chalk, and the final group drawing circles with water.

▶ Challenge pairs of children in the 'paint' group to paint different sized circles, going from small to as big as possible. The first child paints a circle; the second circle paints a bigger circle around the first; the first child paints an even bigger circle around the previous two; and so on.

▶ Set the same challenge for the children using the chalks.

▶ Set the children with the water the challenge of 'Who can draw the biggest circle?'

▶ When the children have experimented, give everyone the opportunity to try the other two experiences.

What you could say:

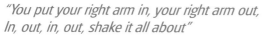

▶ Talk to the children about what they are doing and why.

▶ Make comments about what is happening: "Wow, you are making that green circle a lot smaller than the yellow one."

▶ Ask questions: "I wonder how we could make a circle that touches the fence and the playhouse?"

▶ Model the use of the language of 2D shape and comparison – 'small', 'smaller than', 'smallest'.

Another great idea:

▶ Introduce a version of the traditional favourite, 'The Hokey Cokey'. Children stand in a circle and sing the song:

"You put your right arm in, your right arm out, In, out, in, out, shake it all about"

– following the actions.

Then sing:

"You do the hokey cokey and you turn around,
That's what it's all about!"

– putting hands on hips, wiggling and turning in a circle on the spot.

Finally, sing the words:

Oh, the Hokey Cokey Cokey,
Oh, the Hokey Cokey Cokey,
Oh, the Hokey Cokey Cokey,
That's what it's all about!"

Encourage all children to join hands and move to the centre of the circle.

Continue the song by putting in your left hand, then your right leg, then left leg, and finally your 'whole self'.

SECTION THREE: POSITION, DIRECTION AND MOVEMENT

Our friend Fred

Experienced practitioners know that children are more likely to learn when their emotions are engaged and when they are involved and interested. This activity provides the opportunity to extend the use of a favourite toy.

What's the learning?

Position, direction and movement; making decisions about how to approach a task

What you could provide:

▶ A favourite toy, e.g. Fred the Ted
▶ A digital camera

What you could do:

▶ Ensure that the children are familiar with the use of the digital camera.
▶ Explore the outdoor area and discuss where Fred could be placed – next to the watering can, on the slide, in front of the shed, on top of the crate or under the climbing frame, for example.

▶ Support the children as they place Fred in a chosen position and take a photograph.

▶ Print out the images, and record children's talk about the image in a speech bubble – create a 'Where's Ted?' picture book or a display with the children.

What you could say:

▶ Talk to the children about what they are doing and why.

▶ Introduce and model the use of positional vocabulary: 'under', 'over', 'in front of', 'behind', 'above', 'inside', 'outside', 'next to', 'between'.

▶ Make comments about what is happening: "Ahh, you have put Fred between the two crates."

▶ Ask questions: "I wonder what we could put Fred under?"

▶ Make links with earlier experiences – "Do you remember when we played hot and cold hide and seek?"

Another great idea:

▶ Make a collection of pairs of familiar objects, e.g. two ducks, two cars, two bears, two boxes and two buckets.

▶ Place one of each object on one side of a divider or screen, and the matching object on the other side, so you end up with two symmetrical lines of objects.

▶ Split children into pairs and position each child on either side of the divider. Give instructions as to where each object should be positioned, e.g. "the car should go next to the bear"; "the duck should go in the bucket"; "put the bear between the duck and the box".

▶ Observe as the children place the objects, and then remove the screen to check and compare where each child has positioned them.

▶ Support the children as they place the objects and as they give instructions to each other.

Sally sat-nav

Many young children are familiar with GPS (Global Positioning System) devices, especially in the form of sat-nav instructions during long car journeys. This game builds on these experiences.

What's the learning?

Position, direction and movement; finding new ways to do things

What you could provide:

▶ A megaphone or microphone

▶ Playground chalks

▶ Talking tins

What you could do:

▶ Ensure the children are familiar with navigation systems and choose a name for the children's own navigation system, e.g. 'Sally sat-nav'.

▶ Start out giving simple instructions for all children to try out together, e.g. "Start at the fence; continue straight for ten steps; at the junction, turn left; continue straight for ten steps; you have reached your destination."

▶ With the children, chalk some roadways onto the paved area or tarmac and identify key points or landmarks, e.g. roundabout, petrol station, car park. Encourage the children to work together collaboratively to develop the route.

- Choose a starting point and a destination and, as Sally sat-nav, give directions to individual children. Once they have reached their destination, discuss with the children how there is more than one route from start to finish. What landmarks did they each go past?
- Support children as they take over the role as Sally sat-nav and give directions to others.
- Where appropriate, support children to record directions onto talking tins.

What you could say:

- Talk to children about their own experiences of journey planners and navigation systems.
- Introduce and model the use of the language of position, routes and journeys: 'straight line', 'forwards', 'backwards', 'route', 'pathway', 'start', 'stop', 'position', 'follow', 'finish', 'end', 'start from', 'to', 'along'.
- Support children's growing understanding of turn-taking when speaking, listening and giving and receiving instructions.
- Discuss common navigational instructions: 'start out at', 'turn left', 'continue straight', 'at the roundabout', 'turn right', 'turn around where possible', 'you have reached your destination'.
- Model the use of ordinal numbers when recalling the trip: "What did you do first? And second?"

Another great idea:

- Draw a huge chalked 'island' on the paved area or tarmac.
- Provide potted plants for miniature 'palm trees', an anchor, a treasure chest, and other features children have identified in their pirate role-play.
- This game works best if four pairs of children play. One child in each pair wears a blindfold.
- Each pair chooses a starting point on the island.
- When the children are at their chosen starting point, place the treasure chest somewhere on the 'island'.
- The child not wearing a blindfold in each pair takes turns to give out instructions to their blindfolded partner with the aim of them reaching the treasure chest first, e.g. "Sami, go forward three steps"; "Hussein, turn left, continue four steps." Each 'go' can only be one instruction, including a turn.
- Continue until someone reaches the treasure.

Map reading

This activity offers children the chance to explore the wider environment surrounding your setting and to share this knowledge with others.

What's the learning?

Experiencing position, direction and movement; making decisions about how to approach a task

What you could provide:

▶ Local map
▶ Clipboards
▶ Digital camera or tablet with camera

What you could do:

▶ In a small group, discuss with the children how they arrived at the setting. How many walked? Which route did they take?
▶ Tell them that you will all be going on a group walk and will be taking photographs during your walk.

- ▶ Your aim is to use the photographs to support the children in talking about their discoveries and ideas.

- ▶ During the walk, which need only take about 10 to 15 minutes, draw children's attention to changing direction and to any features, such as a tree or post box. Photograph any features that the children identify. Look out for shapes, road signs, symbols and names.

- ▶ Draw the children's attention to instructions and arrows on the road and reinforce road-safety knowledge.

- ▶ On your return, as a group draw a map of the route you took. You could use a computer drawing programme for this.

- ▶ Print the photographs or display them on the whiteboard. Support the children in providing a commentary.

What you could say:

- ▶ During the walk, refer to the sequence of events: "We came out of the gate and then we crossed the road... and then what did we do?"

- ▶ Make questions and comments such as: "I wonder what the arrow on the road means?" You might need to model the answer initially.

- ▶ Encourage the children to describe any feature of their route and to use everyday words to describe the position of different objects: "The lamp post and the telegraph pole are next to each other."

- ▶ After the walk, trace the route together using Google Earth, as well as on a printed map.

Another great idea:

- ▶ On a large piece of paper, lay out the photographs in route order and connect them with a pathway. This will make the walk into your own photographic map, which you could then turn into a board game.

- ▶ To make the board game, draw squares along the pathway between the photographs. Decide on 'Start' and 'Finish' squares, and provide dice and counters. Explain the rules to the children: if you land on a photograph you have to describe what is in the photograph.

- ▶ Build a 3D model of the route using houses or shops made from recycled boxes, and add small-world people as characters.

Bee-Bot boogie

Give children the opportunity to explore programmable toys and practise giving instructions.

What's the learning?

Position and direction; checking how well things are going

What you could provide:

▶ Bee-Bots (or similar programmable toys)

▶ Marker pens in assorted colours, one attached to each Bee-Bot

▶ Large pieces of paper

What you could do:

▶ Explain the functions of the different keys on the Bee-Bot – focus particularly on the 'clear' function and the use of the direction keys.

▶ Demonstrate how to program the Bee-Bot to move from one place to another.

► Split the children into pairs and provide each pair with a sheet of paper, which has two points marked on it: 'Home' and 'Nursery'. Ask them to program their Bee-Bot and set their toy on its journey from home to nursery. Each Bee-Bot has a different coloured marker pen so that journeys can be compared.

► Observe the strategies children use. At the end, look at the different coloured lines together and note which children compare the difference between the Bee-Bot journeys.

► Introduce more complex routes, e.g. mark out a journey with points 1, 2, 3 and 4, and support children as they program the toys to travel the whole route in one uninterrupted trip.

What you could say:

► Make comments on the movement patterns that the toys make, such as: "Oh look – mine keeps going backwards!"

► Think aloud by making comments such as "I wonder why the blue and green movement lines are so similar, and why the red and purple ones are very different?"

► Challenge children to extend their thinking and mathematical language by asking questions such as: "Is there another route that also goes past points 1, 2, 3 and 4?"

► Talk about how they could investigate how far the Bee-Bot travels for each move.

Another great idea:

► Introduce 'Bee-Bot shopping' to the children. Attach a cardboard box to the back of the Bee-Bot.

► Write a short shopping list, e.g. '1 box of cereal, 6 stamps, 1 train ticket'.

► Stick photos of a supermarket, a post office and a train station onto a large sheet of paper.

► Support the children as they plan a route for their Bee-Bot, with the aim of purchasing all of the items on the shopping list.

Trail blazing

Following a trail provides children with a range of learning opportunities. The scope is endless, and trails can be laid to suit a particular topic or can be invented by the children for each other to follow.

What's the learning?

Position and direction; changing strategy as needed

What you could provide:

▶ Footprint outlines cut from paper and laminated

▶ Masking tape

▶ Chalk

▶ Small sticks

▶ A collection of large objects not normally seen in the chosen context

▶ Clipboards

▶ Pencils

▶ Treasure chest containing shiny counters

What you could do:

▶ Use the laminated paper footprints to make a trail in the outdoor area that children can follow. Make sure it starts in a well-used part of the area such as the climbing frame, and finishes in a quieter space, for instance, next to a tree or bush.

▶ Position the treasure chest at the end of the trail, and lightly camouflage it, e.g. with leaves.

▶ Add objects along the route that are likely to encourage exploration of shape and space, such as a hoop suspended from a bush, or a large bucket hanging upside down on a standing spade. Also dot natural items such as pebbles and pine cones along the trail.

▶ Explain to the children that they are going to follow the trail to find the hidden treasure chest. Suggest that they look for unusual things along the route. They should also collect any natural items that they see along the way. Let them know that if they find treasure at the end of the trail they can take one piece, but must put something else in its place that they have found along the way, such as a stone or a shell.

▶ Help the children who return with treasure to explain to the group what route they followed, what turns there were and whether they went past anything twice, in different directions.

▶ Develop the trail by using arrows assembled with sticks, or chalk arrows on the ground instead of footprints.

▶ Invite the children to lay their own trail for their friend to follow. Encourage the use of positional language and support them in their directional skills.

What you could say:

▶ As the children follow the trail, support discussions about the route they are taking and why.

▶ Encourage the children to use everyday words to describe the position of objects they see along the trail, and to explore these objects. Emphasise that it is not about who reaches the treasure in the quickest time.

▶ Afterwards, ask open questions such as: "Can you explain how you knew which direction to go in?"

▶ Make statements and ask questions such as: "What could we do to remember which way you went?"

Another great idea:

▶ In the outdoor area, with the help of the children, chalk or paint a street floor plan for them to use with toy cars. Resource with models of buildings and small world figures. Explore different routes and turns.

▶ Introduce one-way streets and barriers so that new routes have to be found. Involve children in explaining how to get from one place to another.

▶ Establish pedestrian routes and crossings and talk about turning right and left. Make sure that clipboards and pencils are available for drawing routes. Use cut-out arrows as directional signs.

SECTION FOUR: PATTERN AND SYMMETRY

The mad hatter

Many young children love to play dressing-up, and are often particularly fond of accessorising! This experience gives them an opportunity to think about similarities and differences and to investigate repeating patterns.

What's the learning?

Pattern; descriptive language; making predictions

What you could provide:

▶ A collection of interesting hats, with similarities between them

▶ Music and method of playing

What you could do:

▶ Look at the hats together, taking time to discuss them.

▶ Encourage every child to choose one hat and wear it.

▶ Choose four children who are wearing hats that form a simple repeating pattern, e.g. blue hat, red hat, blue hat, red hat – or woolly hat, cap, woolly hat, cap.

- ▶ Ask the other children to look carefully at the hats, and see if they can spot the pattern. Then ask children to predict: "Do you think you could be the next hat in this repeating pattern?" Let one child have a go – let him or her choose where to stand, and then ask the other children: "Do you think this is still the same repeating pattern?" Ask the child what they think the pattern is, then confirm, or else add the next hat in the pattern and ask them to reconsider.

- ▶ Note how children make decisions about how to approach the task, and observe the strategies they use to make predictions.

What you could say:

- ▶ Introduce and model the use of descriptive vocabulary: "This is my favourite hat; it is woolly and stripy."

- ▶ Discuss the similarities between two hats: "Can you tell me one thing that is the same about these two hats?"

- ▶ Support children's own conversations about what they are doing and why.

- ▶ Help children to express their mathematical thinking as they problem-solve when predicting the next object in a repeating pattern: "What do you think is the next hat in this pattern?"; "Why do you think that?"

- ▶ Support the children as they describe and discuss the hats and use simple words to describe the pattern.

Another great idea:

- ▶ Play 'The Hat Game', a variation of 'Musical Chairs'.

- ▶ Place as many hats as there are children in a long row. Ask each child to stand next to a hat.

- ▶ When you start playing the music, encourage the children to walk around the hats, moving clockwise.

- ▶ When the music stops, each child should put on the hat nearest to them.

- ▶ Walk down the line and ask each child to say one thing about the hat they are wearing.

- ▶ Remove two hats and continue – the children without a hat should sit in a line where their hats were.

- ▶ Continue until there are only two children and one hat – the children have to walk around the hat and the children sitting down. The child who picks up the hat first when the music stops wins.

Double trouble

Give children the opportunity to get active outdoors and find out more about what their bodies can do!

What's the learning?

Symmetry; planning how to reach a goal; thinking of ideas

What you could provide:

▶ A grassy area

▶ Lengths of tape, each a little over a metre long

▶ A digital camera

What you could do:

▶ Ensure the children are beginning to be familiar with points of symmetry. Discuss symmetrical designs with them prior to this activity: experiment with folded paintings and mirrors.

▶ Model symmetry using bodies – pick two volunteers to stand upright, facing each other. As one child puts out an arm, the other does the same; one steps back with one foot, the other reflects the movement. Always ensure that the children stay touching.

▶ Divide the children into pairs and give each pair a length of tape. Set them the challenge of creating a symmetrical design with their bodies: one child makes a body shape on one side of the stretched-out tape (on the ground works well); the second child studies and then attempts to recreate on the other side of the tape.

▶ Observe which children use a 'trial and error' approach and which children try to predict the way in which way to position their bodies.

▶ Take photos of the children, print out and give them the opportunity to discuss.

▶ Revisit the experience on another day, using the images as prompts.

▶ When the children gain confidence, extend the activity to include groups of four or more.

What you could say:

▶ Model the use of positional language and the language of symmetry.

▶ Ask questions such as: "Are you sure that your legs are symmetrical?"

▶ Talk about the photos: "Is this symmetrical?" "If not, why isn't it symmetrical? What could be changed?"

▶ Make connections with children's earlier experiences (e.g. using mirrors to create symmetrical images). Are our faces actually symmetrical?

▶ Provide scaffolding for children's own questions and support them as they comment and answer each other's questions.

Another great idea:

▶ Set a 'Statue Challenge' with the children – divide into groups of three. In each group, one child should be the 'artist' and two children should form a symmetrical 'statue'. The role of the artist is to give each of the other two children instructions, in order to create the symmetrical statue.

▶ Encourage the children to hold their positions and select another two children to be 'art critics', whose role is to look at the statues one at a time and talk about which parts are symmetrical and which parts are not. Ask them to make suggestions about how the 'statues' could change any non-symmetrical elements to become symmetrical.

Puffy paint

Using a flour and water mixture to squirt patterns, squiggles and shapes onto a large sheet outdoors is immensely satisfying for both children and adults! Talk about how the shapes rise after they have dried.

What's the learning?

Pattern and 2D shape; having their own ideas

What you could provide:

▶ One cup of self-raising flour, one cup of salt and one cup of water

▶ Rotary or wire balloon whisk

▶ One large jug, several small jugs (one per child) and spoons

▶ A selection of different coloured ready-mixed paints

▶ Squeezy bottles (one per child)

▶ A large sheet, pegged on an outside washing line with newspaper on the ground to catch any drips

What you could do:

▶ Help the children to whisk the flour, salt and water together in a large jug.

- ▶ When the mixture is runny, pour it into separate small jugs, one per child.
- ▶ Encourage the children to choose a colour of paint and add a small amount to their mixture, stirring it with a spoon.
- ▶ When the paint is stirred through, help children to pour their mixtures into squeezy bottles.
- ▶ Supervise the children as they squirt the paint onto the sheet that is hanging over the washing line using large arm movements.
- ▶ Model how to create curved and straight lines and 2D shapes.
- ▶ Support children in making a group pattern by repeating the squiggles or shapes across the sheet.
- ▶ Encourage children to explore and experiment with pattern independently.
- ▶ When the activity is finished, leave the sheet to dry. As the paint dries it will puff up, giving a 3D finish to the artwork.

What you could say:

- ▶ Describe the lines the children are squirting onto the sheet, identifying whether they are straight, curved or zigzagged.
- ▶ Extend children's vocabulary by using shape words and descriptive words such as 'squelchy', 'squidgy' and 'slippery'.
- ▶ Make supportive statements such as: "I am sure you will be able to continue the pattern. I think you might be about to paint a blue diamond next?"

Another great idea:

- ▶ Instead of using squeezy bottles to squirt the paint, use paintbrushes, paper and individual paint pots.
- ▶ Dry the pictures near a heat source such as a radiator or leave them out in the sun to speed up the drying process and watch the paint rise.
- ▶ Continue the focus on texture by making paper pulp. Together, shred or tear up cardboard egg boxes into a plastic washing up bowl. Add water, and together squash and squeeze the cardboard to make a pulp.
- ▶ Mould the pulp into 3D shapes. Discuss the different features of the shapes the children make. Decorate the shapes with ready-mixed paint – this will help preserve the designs.

Pulled-string symmetry

This activity gives children the opportunity to experience symmetry in an interesting way and create some particularly lovely designs, which look great covering a large display board or when used as covers for children's individual learning folders.

What's the learning?

Creating a symmetrical design; finding new ways to do things

What you could provide:

▶ Ready-mixed paint

▶ Small polystyrene or plastic food trays

▶ Sheets of A4 paper

▶ Thick string and scissors

▶ Rulers or measuring tapes

▶ Paint rollers

What you could do:

▶ Help the children to fold the sheets of paper in half and cut the string in lengths of about 20cm.

▶ Assist in pouring the paint into the trays – one colour per tray.

- Support the children as they each submerge a piece of string in the paint, leaving the end of the string over the side so that it is paint-free.
- Encourage each child to open up one half of a folded sheet of paper. Remove the string from the paint and arrange the piece of string on the paper.
- Make sure that the clean end of the string hangs out from the bottom of the paper.
- Support them in closing the paper and pressing down on it with a hand or roller. Then, with the paper still folded and the hand or roller still pressing down, they should pull out the string.
- Open out the paper and leave the design to dry. Most children enjoy doing this activity several times, so make sure that there is enough paint and paper available.
- When the paint is dry, look at the pulled design on one side of the page and the reflected symmetrical image on the other side of the paper.
- Some children may like to draw in the line of symmetry along the fold of the paper.

What you could say:

- Discuss the designs with the children. Focus on identifying the movement of the string and the symmetry of the patterns.
- Throughout your conversation, introduce words such as 'reflection', 'opposite', 'whole', 'downwards', 'upwards' and 'symmetrical'.
- Identify and talk about symmetrical patterns in the environment. Observing that the two halves of some objects are the same is the beginning of an understanding of symmetry.

Another great idea:

- Make a shape on one half of a pinboard using pins and coloured hair elastics. Support children in making a reflection of that shape. Draw their attention to how many sides the shape has and use their experience of working with mirrors to talk about reflections.
- Together, thread symmetrical bead patterns onto a string. Thread a large bead at the centre as a mirror point and suggest that the children take it in turns to thread identical beads either side of the large bead.
- When a group is involved in printing using vegetables or shapes, draw their attention to the symmetrical properties of the patterns that they are creating.

Mirror the light

Children often notice and comment on the sunlight as it shines through the window. Use this interest to give children more experience of using mirrors to produce symmetrical images.

What's the learning?

Pattern, movement and symmetry; finding out and exploring

What you could provide:

- ▶ A variety of hand-held mirrors
- ▶ Coloured plastic shapes
- ▶ A collection of everyday objects
- ▶ A roll of wrapping paper with a repeating pattern
- ▶ Pattern blocks

What you could do:

- ▶ On a sunny day, invite the children to look for the sunlight indoors and see if they can stand in or put their hand in the ray of light.

- Give out the mirrors and demonstrate how to reflect the sunlight on the walls and ceiling. (Remind them not to direct the sunlight at anything flammable for any length of time!)

- Challenge the children to get the sunlight to dance across the room using their mirror.

- When the children have played with and are becoming expert at handling the mirrors, suggest they use them to reflect objects and plastic shapes. Demonstrate how each child can place their mirror against an object or shape in order to see the whole shape. Can children who are looking at the same type of shape move their mirrors so they each see the same image in the reflection?

- Use wrapping paper with symmetrical patterns and encourage the children to play with the mirrors and wrapping paper, both identifying and changing the pattern.

- Offer pattern blocks for the children to create patterns with. Encourage them to try reflecting or changing the patterns using mirrors.

What you could say:

- Discuss real life 'flip' movements with the children, such as turning over in bed or tossing pancakes.

- Involve children in talking about patterns and shapes and notice which children experiment by putting different shapes together to create a pattern.

- Ask questions such as: "Can you describe the pattern you've made?" "Where should I put the mirror to reflect your pattern?"

Another great idea:

- Resource the creative area with mirror tiles as bases for the children to create their patterns on.

- Hang prisms in different places in the setting to reflect the light and create rainbows.

- Create a fantasy area in a corridor or wide doorway that children can pass through. Decorate with acrylic mirrors and silver foil, and put shiny confetti and sequins in jars. Use silver lurex fabric as a floor covering. Resource with kaleidoscopes and hinge small mirrors together in order for children to be able to experience symmetry and early angle ideas.

Musical patterns

Children's earliest experiences of pattern are often through the repetitive rhythms and phrases of rhymes and songs. Extend these experiences by resourcing the music area with rhythm band instruments to involve the children in making music.

What's the learning?

Pattern and symmetry; making links; noticing patterns in their experience

What you could provide:

▶ Instruments such as drums, shakers, bells and sticks

▶ Dried beans in plastic containers

What you could do:

▶ Sound and movement will often emphasise and enhance the repetitive pattern in a song or rhyme, so start by inventing repeating sound patterns using claps, knee slaps, jumps and other body music.

▶ Emphasise the pattern of the sounds and identify the repetition for the children. You could link this with saying the words out loud as children make the sounds, e.g. 'Clap, slap, jump, clap'.

▶ Together, sing a song the children are familiar with such as 'Heads, shoulders, knees and toes' and set up an early years' band to accompany the singing and actions of the rest of the group.

▶ Support the children in taking turns at being the conductor of the band. Decide together what signals the band leader will make to stop and start the music and to increase and decrease the volume and pace of the music.

▶ Encourage the children to also take turns in being the person giving movement instructions and the person directing the singing. Every child should get experience in both following and carrying out visual instructions for moving and turning. Draw their attention to the symmetry in their movements.

What you could say:

▶ "Listen... can you hear the pattern of the sounds? Would anyone like to say what the pattern is?"

▶ "Has anyone got any ideas about what signal the conductor should make if he wants us play faster or slower?"

▶ Encourage the use of descriptive language.

▶ Involve the children's ideas and summarise them as you extend the activity and their musical experiences.

Another great idea:

▶ Promote spontaneous music in play situations by encouraging children to make their own musical 'shaker' instruments using 1-litre plastic milk containers. Provide stickers and ribbons for each child to decorate the outside of their milk bottle, then support them in counting out some small gravel stones for inside their shaker, before tightening the bottle top. The handles on the milk bottle will make it easy for the children to control the speed and movement of the shaker.

▶ Together, explore the look and feel of the instruments to involve, motivate and sustain the interest of the children.

Nature watch

Young children need time and space to handle and play with lots of different types of shapes and to observe symmetry in nature and natural objects.

What's the learning?

Symmetry; finding out and exploring

What you could provide:

▶ Small woollen blankets

▶ Straight branches

▶ Twigs, leaves, shells, pebbles, gravel, flowers, fir cones, conkers and other natural materials

▶ Wooden trays and wicker baskets

▶ Large child-safe mirrors

▶ A digital camera

What you could do:

▶ Present the materials in wicker baskets and on wooden trays.

▶ Observe, wait and listen to see what the children do with the materials – do they sort them or do they begin to make patterns or designs? Are they using the mirrors?

- ▶ Talk to the children and remind them about symmetry – model the use of the mirrors.
- ▶ For children who have decided to use a straight branch as a line of symmetry, support them in mirroring the design on the other side of the branch – using the mirror if necessary.
- ▶ Support the children as they take a photograph of their symmetrical design.
- ▶ Print out the photos of the designs with the children and act as a scribe to record what they say about their designs, noting any mathematical language used.

What you could say:

- ▶ Talk to the children about things that are the same and things that are different. Discuss objects that are not the same but are similar.
- ▶ Model the use of the language of flat shapes: 'circle', 'triangle', 'square', 'rectangle', 'side', 'corner', 'straight', 'round'.
- ▶ Talk to the children about irregular shapes.
- ▶ Discuss the symmetrical nature of some natural objects and the irregular nature of others. What makes a symmetrical design?
- ▶ Ask children about what they are doing and why – talk to them about their designs or repeating patterns.
- ▶ Support the children as they describe their own patterns, or model talking about them, adding descriptive vocabulary.
- ▶ Use positional language as the children create their designs, e.g. 'next to', 'over', 'under', 'position' and 'between'.

Another great idea:

- ▶ Make a collection of natural objects and opaque materials – skeleton leaves, netting, coloured acetate and gauze, with the children.
- ▶ Encourage the children as they create a unique design using the materials.
- ▶ Use a colour photocopier to copy the design onto acetate film and then place the printed acetate onto a light box.
- ▶ Support the children as they use more irregular objects to create a symmetrical design. How many different symmetrical designs can be created?
- ▶ Alternatively, create a similar experience using whiteboard software which features images of real objects.

Follow the leader

What makes playing outdoors such fun? For many children, it is the chance to move around, make noise and interact with friends – and that's why this game is likely to be a firm favourite.

What's the learning?

Pattern; making links and noticing patterns

What you could provide:

▶ An outdoor place large enough for a number of children to move around freely

What you could do:

▶ Give the children lots of opportunities to explore moving in different ways – jumping, hopping, star jumps, leaping from one foot to the other, etc.

▶ Ask one of the children to model a move and see if the others can copy – name the moves together.

- ▶ Now create a pattern of moves together, e.g. hop, hop, jump, hop, hop, jump.
- ▶ Act as the 'leader' as the group moves around the outdoor area in a line.
- ▶ When the leader stops and creates a new pattern of movements, e.g. star jump, star jump, leap, hop, star jump, start jump, leap, hop, the other children must follow the action. After a couple of rounds, let a child take the lead.
- ▶ Observe the children and see who creates a movement pattern independently and who needs support. Note who continues a pattern and who innovates.

What you could say:

- ▶ Talk to the children about what they are doing, supporting them to verbalise their movements.
- ▶ Make comments about what is happening: "Wow, you are jumping and turning at the same time – that's great!"
- ▶ Ask questions: "So, if you start on two feet, then land on one, what could we call that?"
- ▶ Make links with earlier experiences: "Do you remember when we played musical bumps, moving in different ways?"

Another great idea:

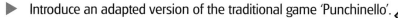
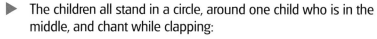

- ▶ Introduce an adapted version of the traditional game 'Punchinello'.
- ▶ The children all stand in a circle, around one child who is in the middle, and chant while clapping:

> Who goes there, Punchinello little fellow?
>
> Who goes there, Punchinello little dear?
>
> What can you do, Punchinello little fellow?
>
> What can you do, Punchinello little dear?

(The child in the middle creates a movement pattern, e.g. clap, clap, wave, wave, clap, clap, wave, wave.)

> We'll do it too, Punchinello little fellow,
>
> We'll do it too, Punchinello little dear!

(All the children in the circle copy the movement pattern.)

- ▶ The child in the middle chooses a friend and they swap places so that there is a new Punchinello.

Further reading and resources

Andrews, A. and Trafton, P. (2002) 'Little Kids: Powerful problem solvers', Heinnemann

Beckley, P. et al (2010) 'Problem Solving, Reasoning and Numeracy', Continuum

Bennett, E. and Weidner, J. (2011) 'Everyday Maths through Everyday Provision: Developing opportunities for maths in the Early Years', Routledge

Bennett, E. and Weidner, J. (2013) 'The Building Blocks of Everyday Maths: Bringing key concepts to life in the Early Years and Key Stage 1', Routledge

Dancer, J. and Skinner, C. (2014) 'The Little Book of Maths Problem-Solving', Featherstone

Skinner, C. and Stevens, J. (2013) 'Foundations of Mathematics: An active approach to number, shape and measures in the Early Years', Featherstone

Skinner, C. (2015) 'Maths Outdoors', BEAM

Skinner, C. and Stevens, J. (2014) 'The Little Book of Measures', Featherstone

Smith, S. (2006) 'Early Childhood Mathematics', Pearson

Stevens, J. (2013) 'Maths Development Wheel: A guide for parents, careers and practitioners', Early Years and Childcare Publishing Partnerships, KMMD Publishing

Stevens, J. (2008) 'Maths in Stories', BEAM

Stevens, J. (2009) 'Maths Now: The definitive guide to maths in the Early Years Foundation Stage', BEAM 2009

www.nrich.maths.org